C000257617

Gold, Frankincen And Myrrh

by Alison Hedger

The traditional Biblical Nativity story, retold with seven new songs especially written for young children.

Duration approx. 20 mins.

For Pre-school children.
Early Key Stage 1 and Special Education Units

TEACHER'S BOOK
Complete with script, piano accompaniment, vocal line and chord symbols.

SONGS

1. A Long, Long Time Ago
2. Lots And Lots Of People
3. Shepherds Sitting On A Hill
4. Journey's End
5. Gold, Frankincense And Myrrh *with optional metallophone part*
6. Sleep My Little One
7. We Wish You *with clapping and optional percussion*

A matching tape cassette of the music for rehearsals and performances is available, Order No. GA10686, with narration and singing included on side A and omitted on side B.

© Copyright 1993 Golden Apple Productions
A division of Chester Music Limited
8/9 Frith Street, London W1V 5TZ

Order No. GA10613
ISBN 0-7119-3380-4

GOLD, FRANKINCENSE and MYRRH is intended to give the very youngest of children musically satisfying songs which are easily learnt and fun to sing.

The Christmas Nativity is presented in story form. This makes the work very versatile. An adult may read the narrative leaving the young singers to enjoy the songs as the story unfolds. Alternatively, the children can build up the Nativity tableau and act out the story as it is related. Simple speech parts can be written into the script for use by slightly older children, or the narration can be given to fluent readers.

The companion tape to GOLD, FRANKINCENSE and MYRRH has the narration word for word, included on side A. A child may follow the story from the book whilst listening to the tape. This adds another dimension to the work. It can be an aid to reading and also an entertainment.

The A side of the tape has the words of the songs included, but the B side of the tape has the music accompaniment only, with no vocal line. This makes the tape very useful for performances where no pianist is available.

The choice of how to use this book is up to individuals. Hence the deliberate omission of "stage" directions, entrances and exits etc.

It is hoped that the youngest of children in playgroups, at home, in nursery and reception classes and in the early stages of Key Stage I will enjoy singing these songs and hearing the story of the first Christmas.

This mini-musical will also have a valuable place within Special Education Units, where longer, more complicated songs can be a problem.

"I try and remember each Christmas, that for very young children, this may be the first Christmas that is remembered for the rest of their lives. May it be a truly happy occasion for them. May you too, enjoy the songs."

Best wishes,

Alison Hedger

INTRODUCTION

Repeat as necessary

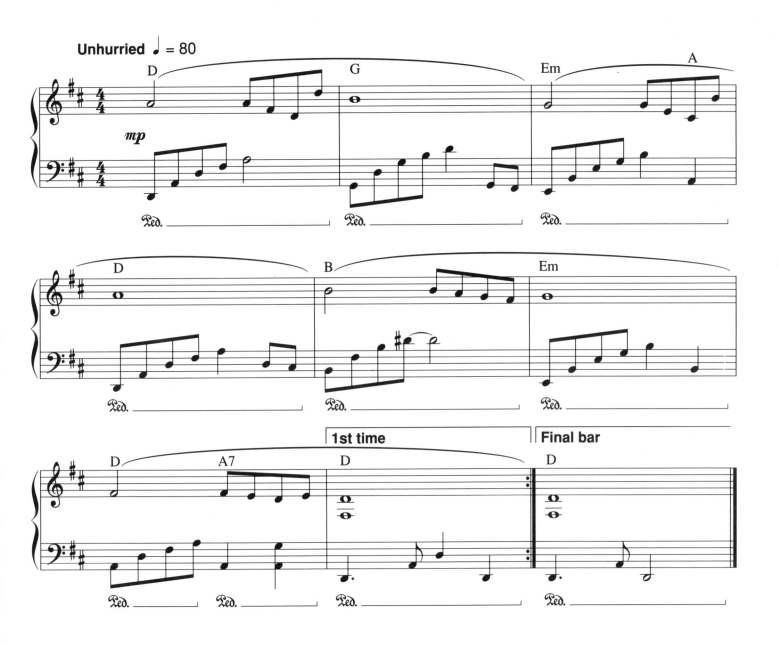

A long, long time ago, in the far away town of Nazareth, there lived a young woman called Mary. One day an angel came to her and told her some exciting news.

A LONG, LONG TIME AGO
(Verses 1–4)

♪ 1. A long, long time ago
There lived a girl called Mary.
A long, long time ago.

2. An angel came to her
And said she'd have God's baby.
A long, long time ago.

Mary was going to have a special baby boy and she was to call him Jesus. She loved a carpenter called Joseph and he wanted to look after her, so they were married.

♪ 3. A long, long time ago
There lived a man called Joseph.
A long, long time ago.

4. He looked after his wife
Who was to have God's baby.
A long, long time ago.

Now at this time, a Roman Emperor was in charge of the country and he ordered everyone to go to their home town to pay their taxes. Joseph came from Bethlehem, so that is where he and Mary had to go.

As there were no cars or trains or buses most people had to walk. Mary was lucky, she had a donkey to ride on.

5. A long, long time ago
   They went to Bethlehem.
   A long, long time ago.

6. A donkey carried Mary
   Along the bumpy roads.
   A long, long time ago.

SONG ONE

A LONG, LONG TIME AGO
(Verses 5 and 6)

went to Beth - le - hem.___ A long, long time a - go.

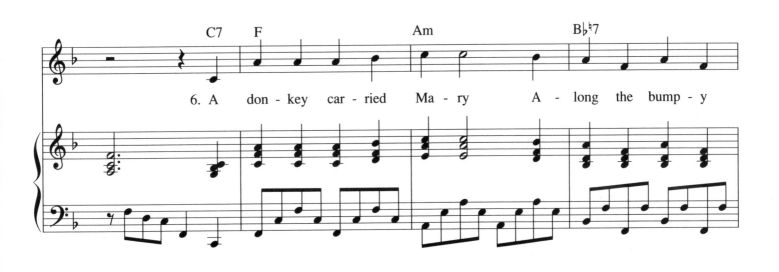

6. A don - key car - ried Ma - ry A - long the bump - y

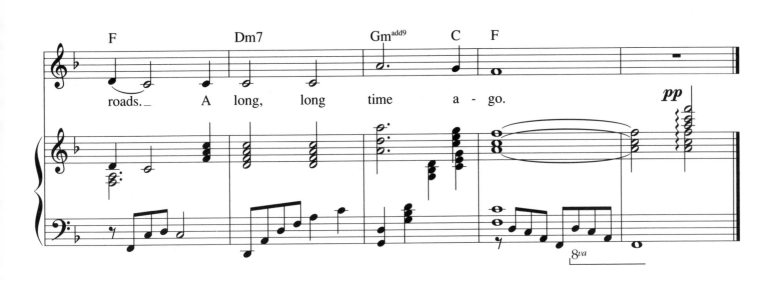

roads.___ A long, long time a - go.

After a very long journey they arrived in Bethlehem, but so had many other people and they all needed somewhere to stay.

♪   1. Lots and lots of people, coming into town
Looking for somewhere to stay.
Lots and lots of people, coming into town
Looking for somewhere to stay.

Have you any room please?
Have you any room please?
Have you any room please?
We're looking for somewhere to stay.

Lots and lots of people, coming into town
Looking for somewhere to stay.

2. Joseph and Mary, coming into town
Looking for somewhere to stay
Joseph and Mary, coming into town
Looking for somewhere to stay.

Have you any room please?
Have you any room please?
Have you any room please?
We're looking for somewhere to stay.

Joseph and Mary, coming into town
Looking for somewhere to stay.
Joseph and Mary, coming into town
Looking for somewhere to stay.

(First bar rhythm for verse 2)

8

SONG TWO

LOTS AND LOTS OF PEOPLE

1. Lots and lots of peo - ple com - ing in - to town Look - ing for some - where to stay.

stay. Have you an - y room please? Have you an - y room please?

Have you an - y room please? We're look - ing for some - where to stay.

No one had room for them until a kind innkeeper, who could see how tired Mary was, showed them to his stable.

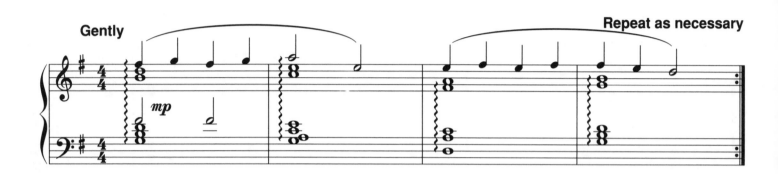

'My animals will keep you warm.'

'Thank you.'

Later that night Mary's baby was born.

On a hillside outside Bethlehem some shepherds were looking after their sheep. Suddenly the night sky lit up and there were angels singing.

'Do not be afraid.'

The angels said 'We have come to tell you good news . . . . . tonight, a baby King has been born in Bethlehem. Go and search for the baby. You will find him lying in a manger.'

SHEPHERDS SITTING ON A HILL

(The guitar chords shown have been simplified)

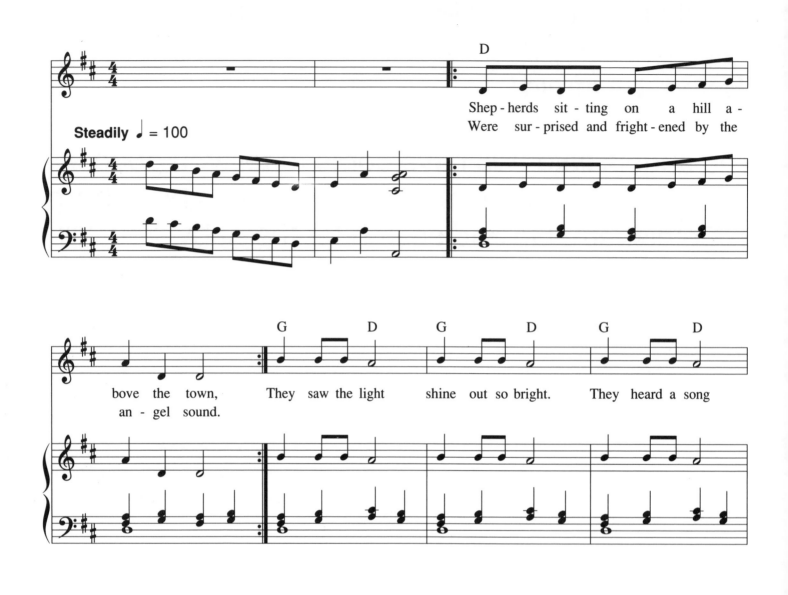

Shep - herds sit - ting on a hill a -
Were sur - prised and fright - ened by the

bove the town, They saw the light shine out so bright. They heard a song
an - gel sound.

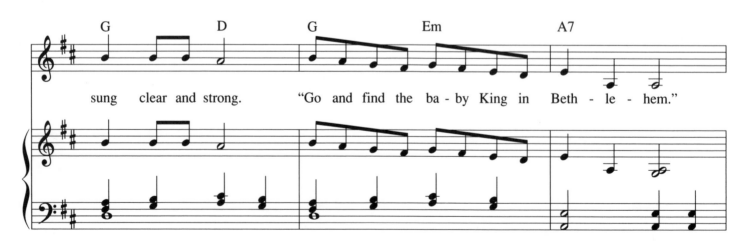

sung clear and strong. "Go and find the ba - by King in Beth - le - hem."

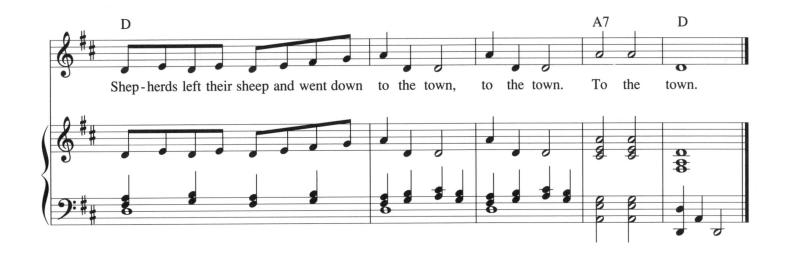

Shepherds sitting on a hill
above the town,
Were surprised and frightened
by the angel sound.

They saw the light
Shine out so bright.
They heard a song
Sung clear and strong.

"Go and find the baby King
in Bethlehem."

Shepherds left their sheep
and went down to the town,
To the town.
To the town.

13

The shepherds left their sheep and hurried to Bethlehem. They found Jesus in the stable just as the angels had said.

 Shepherds sitting on a hill
above the town,
Were surprised and frightened
by the angel sound.

They saw the light
Shine out so bright.
They heard a song
Sung clear and strong.

"Go and find the baby King
in Bethlehem."

Shepherds left their sheep
and went down to the town,
To the town.
To the town.

SONG THREE

SHEPHERDS SITTING ON A HILL

(Repeat)

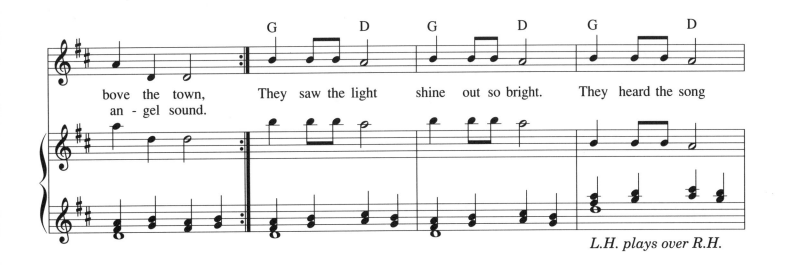

bove the town,
an - gel sound.

They saw the light shine out so bright. They heard the song

L.H. plays over R.H.

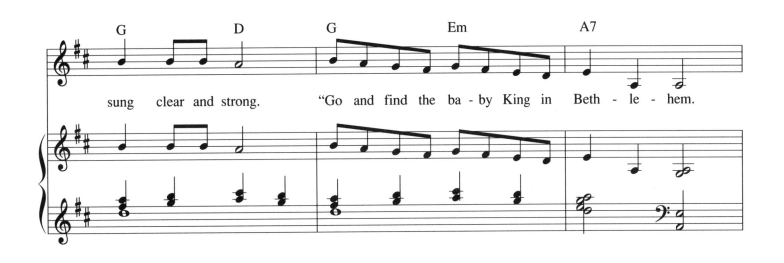

sung clear and strong. "Go and find the ba - by King in Beth - le - hem.

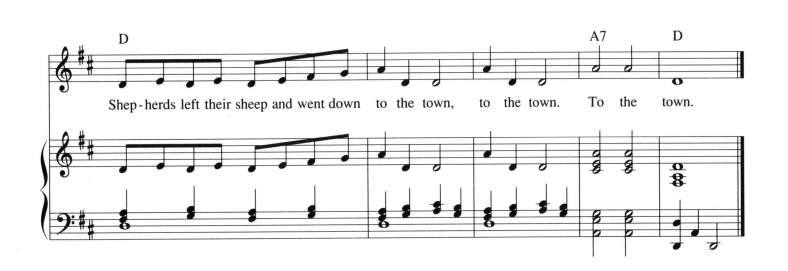

Shep - herds left their sheep and went down to the town, to the town. To the town.

Far away in the East, three wise men
saw a bright new star in the sky.
They knew that it meant a baby King
had been born. They set off on
their camels to follow
the star . . . .
where would it lead them?

♪ 1. Where will it be —
        Journey's end?
        We've got a long way to go   *(Sing verse twice)*
          my friend.

                    2. We have arrived
                        Journey's end.
                        We've brought a gift for you
                          tiny friend.

SONG FOUR

JOURNEY'S END

Lumbering and camel-like! ♩ = 76

1. Where will it be jour - ney's end? We've got a long way to
2. We have ar - rived jour - ney's end. We've brought a gift for you

go my friend.
ti - ny friend.

last time bar

The star stopped above the stable. The three
wise men went quietly inside and found Jesus
in His mother's arms.

They each brought a very precious present for Jesus.
One gave gold, one frankincense, and one myrrh.

♪ Gold, frankincense and myrrh,
Gold, frankincense and myrrh,
Gold, frankincense and myrrh,
Gold, frankincense and myrrh.

(sing through three times)

SONG FIVE GOLD, FRANKINCENSE and MYRRH

The optional metallophone part is best learnt by rote, and can be added to the song wherever desired.

If using older children, try adding a gentle, deep drum ostinato

Mary was very happy to show Jesus to all the visitors. She rocked him gently and sang him a lullaby.

♪ Sleep, sleep, sleep.
Sleep my little one.
Sleep, sleep, sleep.
Your life has just begun.

Close your eyes.
Make no cries.
Snuggle down
Until sunrise.

Sleep, sleep, sleep.
Sleep my little one.
Sleep, sleep, sleep.
Your life has just begun.

SONG SIX   **SLEEP MY LITTLE ONE**

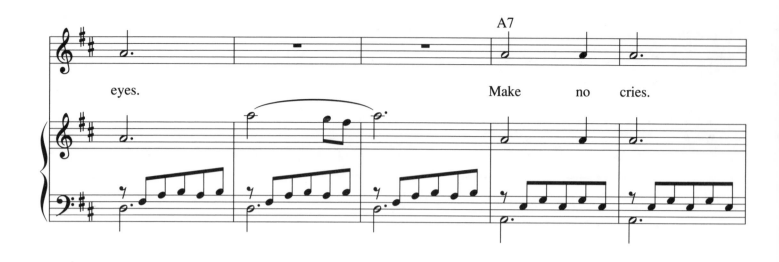

eyes. Make no cries.

Snug - gle down un - til sun -

rise.

All over the world people still tell the Christmas story of how the bright star led the shepherds and the wise men to the stable where Jesus was born.

♪ We wish you a very Merry Christmas
And we wish you a Happy New Year.

SONG SEVEN

WE WISH YOU
(Repeat as necessary)

Children sing through twice, then clap with the words. It may be a good idea to involve parents by asking them to join in with the singing and clapping.

Use percussion instruments as desired. Play along with the words.

THE END

Printed by Caligraving Limited Thetford Norfolk England

10/98 (32111)